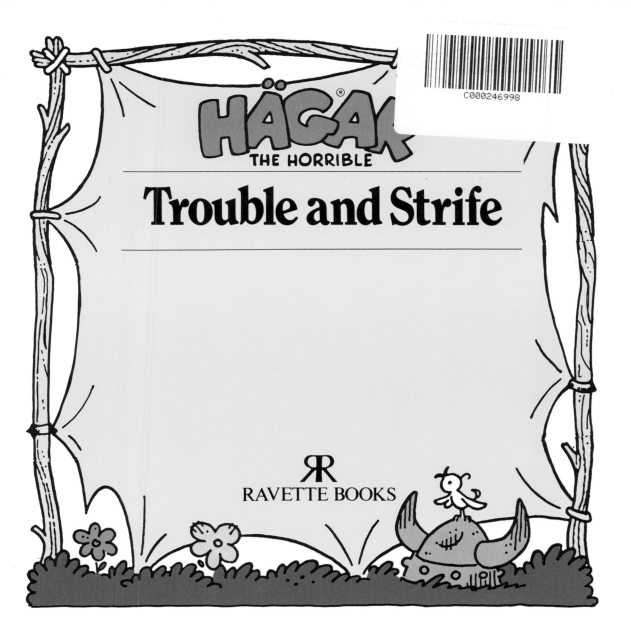

# HÄGAR THE HORRIBLE

# Trouble and Strife

RAVETTE BOOKS

This edition first published by Ravette Books Limited 1989

Printed and Bound
for Ravette Books Limited,
3 Glenside Estate, Star Road, Partridge Green,
Horsham, West Sussex RH13 8RA
by Mateu Cromo Artes Gráfica, s.a.

ISBN: 1 85304 212 9

# A selection of HÄGAR books published by Ravette

**COLOUR THEME BOOKS**  *£2.95 each*
No 1 THE GREAT GOURMET
No 3 TAKES A JOURNEY
No 4 WHO DARES WINS
No 5 CHILD'S PLAY

**POCKET BOOKS**  *£1.95 each*
TRIES AGAIN
HAS A GO
IN A FIX
ON THE RAMPAGE
GETS IT ALL
IN THE ROUGH
LEADS THE WAY
TAKES A BREAK
ALL AT SEA
ON HOLIDAY
TAKES AIM
IN A STEW

**ALBUMS**  *£2.50 each*
THE HERO
LETS HIMSELF GO

**BLACK AND WHITE LANDSCAPES**  *£2.50 each*
MEETS HIS MATCH
IN A HURRY

**COLOUR LANDSCAPES**  *£2.95 each*
TELLS IT LIKE IT IS
NEVER SAY DIE
MAKES AN ENTRANCE
WELCOME HOME

VIKING HANDBOOK  *£3.95*

All these books are available at your local bookshop or newsagent, or can be ordered direct from the publisher. Just tick the titles you require and fill in the form below. Prices and availability subject to change without notice.

---

Ravette Books Limited, 3 Glenside Estate, Star Road, Partridge Green, Horsham, West Sussex RH13 8RA

Please send a cheque or postal order and allow the following for postage and packing. UK: Pocket books – 45p for one book plus 20p for the second book and 15p for each additional book. Landscape series – 50p for one book plus 30p for each additional book. Other titles – 85p for one book plus 60p for each additional book.

Name ...................................................................................................................................................................

Address ...............................................................................................................................................................

.............................................................................................................................................................................